balloon bat beak bee bicycle black boil

cow crocodile crow dalmatian dance

dolphin door drop drum duck egret

eyeglass face fish fly funnel garland

op holey ha ibi eam igloo iguana

p kettle key king kippers kitchen kittens

nandolin map mariner mast mermaids

cissus nasturtium natterjack nectarine

m paper parrot pelican penguin picnic pig

acoon radio rainbow rat river robin sand

ordfish tambourine tight-rope toothbrush

orn universe valentine vase vegetables

atering-can watermelon waves whale

t yak yellow yo-yo zebra zip zoo zoom

Alphabet
GALLERY

Alphabet
GALLERY

AN ABC OF
CONTEMPORARY ILLUSTRATORS

First published in Great Britain 1999
by Mammoth
an imprint of Egmont Children's Books Limited
239 Kensington High Street, London W8 6SA
© copyright in each individual contribution is reserved by the contributor
0 7497 4045 0
A CIP catalogue record for this title is available from the British Library
Printed in Hong Kong

Produced in association with The Dyslexia Institute.
Registered Charity: number 268502

10% of the Publisher's proceeds from the sale
of each copy of the book shall be donated to
The Dyslexia Institute

Jul, 484
£14.99

Alphabet
GALLERY

devised by Gina Pollinger for The Dyslexia Institute

How it came about

In 1997, at Christie's in London, there was a grand charity auction in celebration of The Dyslexia Institute's 25th anniversary. It was intriguingly advertised as 'the rite to rede ORCSHUN'. Inspired by the soundness of the cause, as well as by my own experience (over three decades!) of nurturing and promoting children's books, I responded enthusiastically to the invitation of the Institute's Executive Director, Liz Brooks, to make a 'creative contribution' to the ORCSHUN. That single but remarkable word 'ORCSHUN' sparked a concept: I would approach seven of the finest illustrators in the country and invite each to illustrate a different letter from that word – each letter matching one of their own initials.

The result was truly spectacular, and the framed pictorial letters proved very successful under the hammer on the night. Consequently, with Liz Brooks' encouragement, I determined to seek out a further nineteen illustrators to complete the alphabet.

Thus our star-studded alphabet was conceived and developed. On the day that I received the twenty-sixth piece of artwork, I could suddenly see in my mind's eye that thrilling and significant word, BOOK! The rest is history – or, should I say, history in-the-making!

Gina Pollinger

Gina Pollinger studied English Literature at Oxford and worked as an editor in New York and London before her marriage to fellow literary agent, Murray Pollinger. She is currently on the Advisory Board of the National Year of Reading and received the Eleanor Farjeon Award in 1998 for distinguished services to children's publishing.

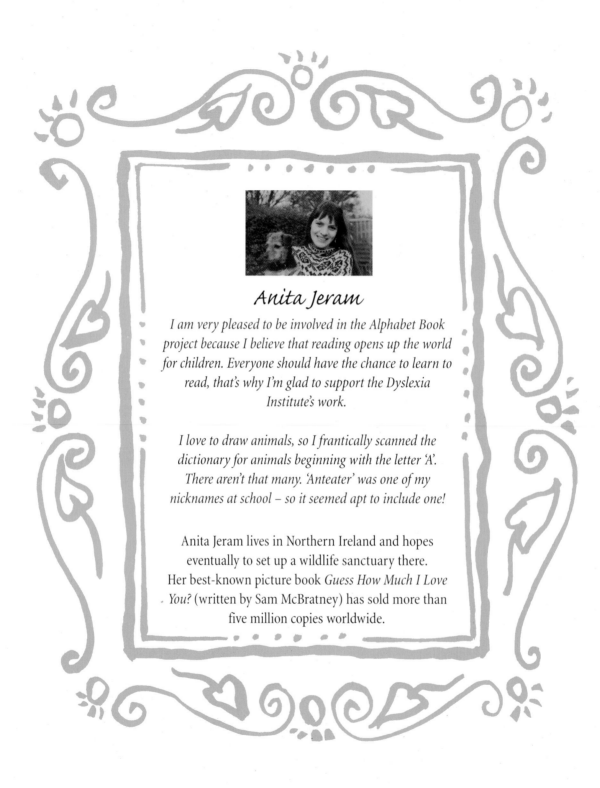

Anita Jeram

I am very pleased to be involved in the Alphabet Book project because I believe that reading opens up the world for children. Everyone should have the chance to learn to read, that's why I'm glad to support the Dyslexia Institute's work.

I love to draw animals, so I frantically scanned the dictionary for animals beginning with the letter 'A'. There aren't that many. 'Anteater' was one of my nicknames at school – so it seemed apt to include one!

Anita Jeram lives in Northern Ireland and hopes eventually to set up a wildlife sanctuary there. Her best-known picture book *Guess How Much I Love You?* (written by Sam McBratney) has sold more than five million copies worldwide.

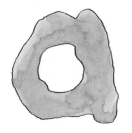

Raymond Briggs

There are bore things beginning with B than any other better in the balphabet. I wanted to put as bany as bossible in the bicture, but to braw them all bould have been bery baborious. Bo I becided to bake all the things as small as bossible to bave babour. Then I thought one thing ought to be bery big bo as to bill up the space. The beasiest thing to braw was a boulder. Anybody ban braw a boulder! Bo then I thought of a boulder bashing flat some of the things bo there would be even bess babour in brawing them. Easy-beasy! (But now I've bot Bs on the brain.)

Raymond Briggs studied at Wimbledon School of Art and the Slade and in 1961 became a Lecturer at the Brighton College of Art. He has produced a stream of innovative and acclaimed picture books including *Father Christmas* and *The Snowman*. One of the best-loved and most controversial illustrators in the world, he has twice won the Kate Greenaway Medal.

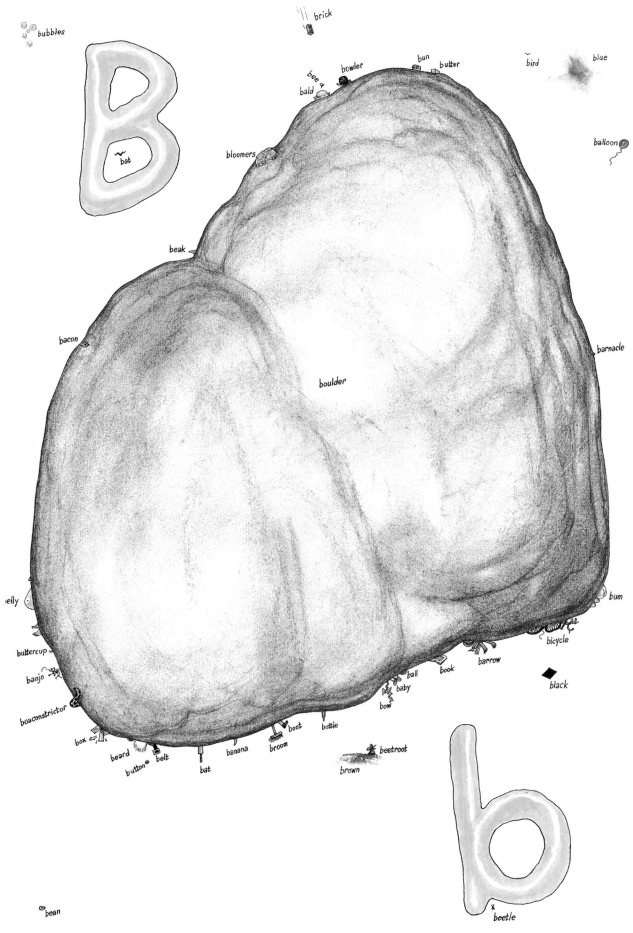

bubbles

brick

B

bat

bee
bald

bowler

bun
butter

bird

blue

balloon

bloomers

beak

bacon

boulder

barnacle

belly

bum

buttercup

bicycle

banjo

barrow

boaconstrictor

book

black

box

ball
baby

beard

bow

broom

bottle

button
belt

bat

banana

beetroot

brown

b

bean

beetle

Raymond Briggs '93

Emma Chichester Clark

I looked up C in the dictionary and wrote a list of all the birds and animals. I wish there had been room for a cassowary, and a cormorant, even for a cauliflower, or a cabbage, but it got crowded and complicated. I couldn't help making another list of my favourite words:

caboose, cacophony, cahoot, coriander, camomile, canoodle, comrade, candour, cantankerous, carbuncle, colombine, concede, calamity, cadence, cup, centipede.

Emma Chichester Clark trained at the Chelsea College of Art and the Royal College of Art where she became a prize-winning pupil of Quentin Blake. In 1988 she won the Mother Goose Award for the most promising newcomer to children's book illustration. Since then she has illustrated a number of classic children's books.

Kady MacDonald Denton

On my desk is a dictionary and in it I knew I would find words beginning with D. I found far too many. It was hard to decide. I wanted twelve images, to make a nice dozen. So I went for a walk around the house and then outside. Many of the things illustrated here I saw on the walk, although not the dinosaur or dolphin or deer; those were the suggestions of some children I met.

Kady MacDonald Denton studied at the University of Toronto and Chelsea School of Art. Since then she has worked on over twenty books, including *Would They Love a Lion?* Kady lives in Manitoba.

Andy Ellis

*Eveline, the enchanted elephant, sat in an English Elm,
eating eggs while exercising her ears. Erik, the elegant elk,
couldn't believe his eyes. It was at that moment that Ethel,
the enervated eagle, delivered an empty envelope to
Eveline. Only later did anyone think to count the eggs.
Just after the idea of the alphabet was suggested to me
I looked out of my window. There was Eveline, sitting
in the branches of the elm tree. Erik and Ethel were
peeking out from the bookshelf. I picked up my pencil
and began to draw.*

Andy Ellis spent several years working as an artist
for children's magazines. Since then he has written
and illustrated numerous children's books as well
as creating animated series for television.

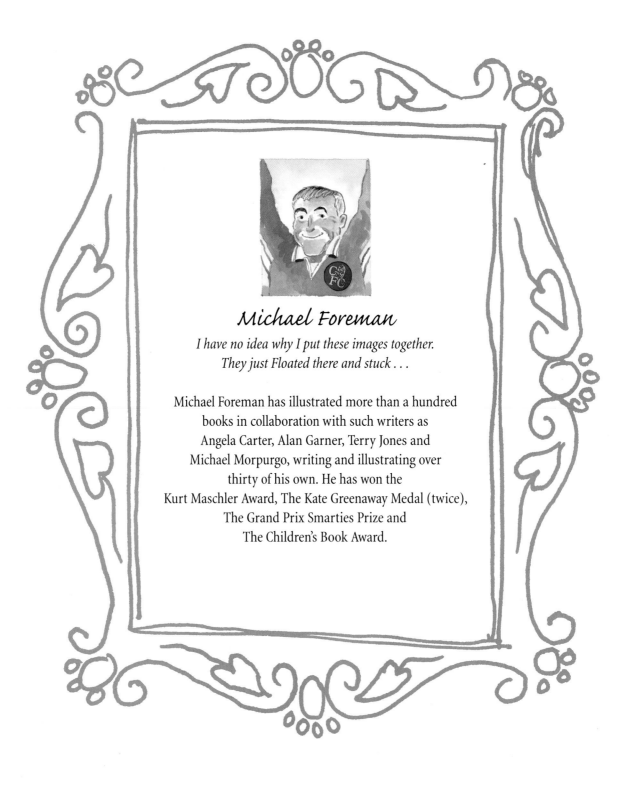

Michael Foreman

I have no idea why I put these images together.
They just Floated there and stuck . . .

Michael Foreman has illustrated more than a hundred
books in collaboration with such writers as
Angela Carter, Alan Garner, Terry Jones and
Michael Morpurgo, writing and illustrating over
thirty of his own. He has won the
Kurt Maschler Award, The Kate Greenaway Medal (twice),
The Grand Prix Smarties Prize and
The Children's Book Award.

Debi Gliori

My first is in grass, but not in lawn.
My second in sunset, but never at dawn.
My third is in more, and also in less.
My fourth not in no, but always in yes.
My fifth, like my fourth, you will have to . . .

Debi Gliori worked as a successful illustrator of
other people's stories before devoting herself to the
writing and illustration of children's picture books.
Mr Bear to the Rescue won the picture book section of the
Children's Book Award, and was shortlisted for the 1997
Kate Greenaway Medal.

Answer: Guess!

G g

J116484

Colin Hawkins

*I think that hogs must be one of my favourite creatures.
I love their sheer delight at looking so comfortably rotund
– a definite 'Let's hog on down, fat is fun' attitude. I love
their passionate snuffling, snorting, grunting, rooting,
questing zest for life. And their absolute gusto; they are the
very best at hogging and always have been.*

In the 1970s Colin and his wife Jacqui began creating
children's books together. This unique collaboration has
produced a stream of exuberant books, including *What's
the Time Mr Wolf*, *Snap! Snap!*, *Monsters and Aliens*,
Witches, *Vampires* and *Pat the Cat*.

Ian Penney

Inspiration immediately ignited innermost imagination initiating idiotic ideas including icing, insects, igloo, ice, invoice, ink, ibis, Indian, instruments, in-tray, iguana, ice cream. Indeed, it is intoxicating.

Ian Penney has illustrated a number of books, including several titles for the National Trust: *The National Trust Book of Nursery Rhymes*, *The National Trust Book of Fairy Tales* and *The National Trust ABC*.

Jill Murphy

*J is a rather formless kind of letter. It's bad enough
having it at the beginning of my name without
illustrating it too! I had been hoping to draw something
nice and cuddly but J is for things like 'jam jar' and 'javelin'.
But then the word 'jaguar' sprang to mind and before I
knew it a jaguar in jersey and jeans was jumping for
joy all over the page.*

Jill Murphy trained in Art and worked in a children's home
before becoming a full-time writer and illustrator.
The Worst Witch stories that she wrote at 17 are loved
by children all over the world. *The Last Noo-noo* won the
under-five category of the 1995 Smarties Book Prize.

J

J

J

j

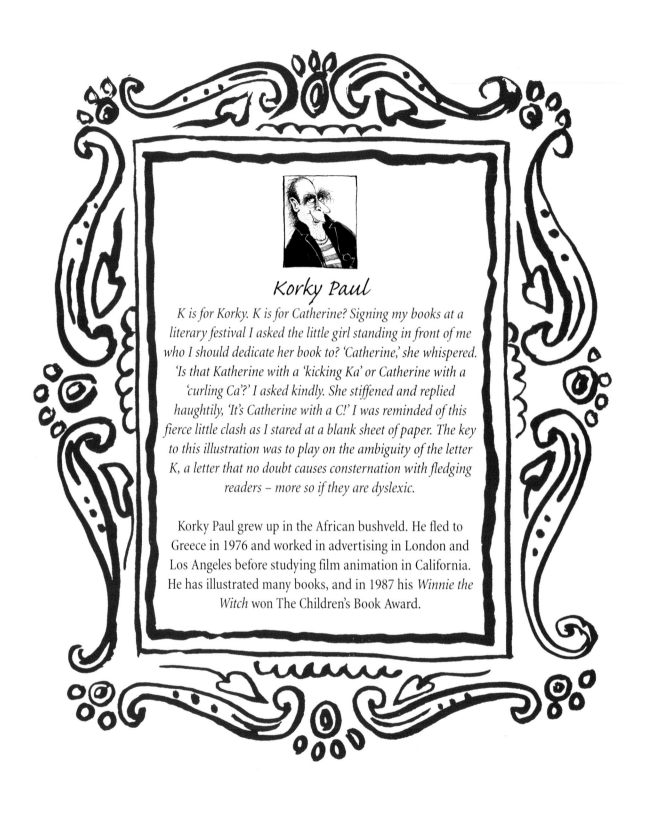

Korky Paul

K is for Korky. K is for Catherine? Signing my books at a literary festival I asked the little girl standing in front of me who I should dedicate her book to? 'Catherine,' she whispered. 'Is that Katherine with a 'kicking Ka' or Catherine with a 'curling Ca'?' I asked kindly. She stiffened and replied haughtily, 'It's Catherine with a C!' I was reminded of this fierce little clash as I stared at a blank sheet of paper. The key to this illustration was to play on the ambiguity of the letter K, a letter that no doubt causes consternation with fledging readers – more so if they are dyslexic.

Korky Paul grew up in the African bushveld. He fled to Greece in 1976 and worked in advertising in London and Los Angeles before studying film animation in California. He has illustrated many books, and in 1987 his *Winnie the Witch* won The Children's Book Award.

PJ Lynch

I was very lucky to get the letter L, it's such a lovely letter for alliteration. I had great fun drawing my lacy, lilac Lion and his legless lady Lizard in lemon.
They are painted loosely in watercolours over a pencil drawing with a few gouache highlights.

P.J. Lynch lives in Dublin and has his studio in a big Georgian house. His first book, *A Bag of Moonshine*, won him the Mother Goose Award and his latest book won him the Kate Greenaway Medal for the second time.

James Mayhew

*I was determined that the various parts of the picture
would make a whole and I was also determined to have
Mermaids. All Mermaids have Mirrors, so that was easy.
And Mermaids are famous for singing, so some Music by
Mozart fitted. The third Mermaid needed something.
I thought of a treasure Map and that led to Money. I put
the mermaids on Mossy rocks in 'la Mer' and filled the sky
with Moonlight and Mist and a small Meteorite. Lastly,
a Mariner stands before the Mast and I hope he and other
viewers of the scene will find Magic in what they see.*

James Mayhew has illustrated many of the great classic
tales. His work for *The Cloth of Dreams* by Jenny Koralek
won him the 1994 New York Times Award for one of the
year's ten best illustrated books.

Nicola Bayley

Unfortunately there were no furry things to illustrate starting with n in my dictionary. In fact I was tempted to do a page of naïve, nasty, needy, nervy and niminy-piminy cats, as cats are what I generally do. In the end I went for a still-life rather than a narrative picture, done in watercolour.

Nicola Bayley was born in Singapore in 1949 and studied at the Royal College of Art under Quentin Blake. Nicola has won many prizes for her exquisite illustrations.
The Mousehole Cat was commended for the Kate Greenaway Medal and turned into a widely-acclaimed animated film.

Helen Oxenbury

'In my Opinion I'm an Original,' said Otto the
Orang-utan, Ogling his Organic Orange.
'Oh dear, I'm Only Ordinary,' cried Oska,
the Obsequious Otter, while the Ostentatious Ostrich
Overtook Ollie the Owl on his Oscillating O.

Helen Oxenbury is one of the world's most popular and
acclaimed children's book illustrators. In 1969 she was
awarded the Kate Greenaway Medal for *The Quangle*
Wangle's Hat. She has also won the British Book Award,
the Kurt Maschler Award, the Smarties Book
Prize and the SHE/W.H.Smith Award.

Patrick Benson

*As soon as I finished this picture I began to find more
wonderful animals whose names begin with the letter P.
My favourites so far are the Potto, a tree-dwelling
member of the loris family from West Africa,
and the Pangolin, a scaly ant-eating animal found
in Asia and Africa.*

Patrick Benson studied classical drawing in Florence, and
attended both Chelsea Art School and St Martin's. In 1989
he won the Mother Goose Award for his illustration of
William Mayne's *Hob* Stories, since when he has gained
further critical acclaim for his collaboration with 25 other
writers, winning the Kurt Maschler Award in 1995.
Patrick lives in the country. Fly fishing is his hobby.

Quentin Blake

I have already done two Alphabet Books so I have some practice at this game. What I did on this occasion was to look up the Q section in a wonderful book called I See All, *which is a kind of pictorial dictionary, and I drew the ones that seemed to go well together and offered the opportunity for me to draw something that I like.*

Quentin Blake started out as a cartoonist for *Punch* with no formal training in illustration. He is now one of the world's best-loved children's illustrators. His picture book, *Clown*, won the Bologna Ragazzi Prize in 1996. Quentin is a visiting professor at the Royal College of Art, and in 1988 was awarded an OBE. In 1999, he became Britain's first Children's Laureate.

Tony Ross

I enjoyed drawing this for such a worthy cause.
There are four letter Rs in the picture, they're pretty obvious,
but can you find seventeen things beginning with R?
Some of them R really sneaky.

Tony Ross trained at the Liverpool School of Art and has worked as a cartoonist, graphic designer, Art Director of an advertising agency and as Senior Lecturer in Art at Manchester Polytechnic. Over the past few years, he has become one of the best-known creators of original and traditional picture books, and the humour and flamboyance of Tony's work has won him worldwide recognition.

Nick Sharratt

I've drawn a saxophone-playing sea horse to celebrate the letter S's slinky shape.

Nick Sharratt has been writing and illustrating children's books since 1991. In this short space of time he has become one of the most well-loved contemporary illustrators. His pictures are renowned for adding zest and appeal to the work of award-winning children's writers and in 1997 his own *Cheese and Tomato Spider* won the Sheffield Children's Book Award.

Carol Thompson

Well, the idea was the easy bit, and I had weeks and weeks to do the artwork. The deadline was marked heavily in red ink on the calendar. Time passes. The phone rings. The Organiser tells me how excited she is at the prospect of receiving my work. My anxiety level soars. I bake some cakes. But I will start tomorrow. Get on with it! Time passes. I trawl the charity shops. One week to go. And still white paper. Panic-stricken, I request that my husband locks me into my studio until it's done. He duly obliges.
It's done. It's finished. Water colour, crayon, collage, pastel, tears, and the final touch of inspiration, a real feather.

Carol Thompson is a freelance artist and illustrator and has illustrated many children's books. *The Busy Baby's Day* series, which she wrote and illustrated, was runner-up in the 1988 Mother Goose Award.

Martin Ursell

*Undaunted and unafraid of U as an unarguably
uninspiring and unpromising letter, I unearthed umpteen
dictionaries, uprooted unusual encyclopaedias and
uncovered the upmost up-to-date authorities until
ultimately I ended up with an undeniably unique,
unexpurgated unit – an unbeaten, unputdownable and
unashamedly 'ultra' list of words beginning with U.
Upstairs I undertook with umber and unbelievable
unctuousness to illustrate it. Undoubtedly the union is
ungrudgingly unmasked opposite.*

Martin Ursell is a prolific and successful children's
illustrator. He was a regular contributor to 'Jackanory'
and his own story *Hairy Hairy* was televised by the BBC.
Martin has also illustrated stories by Dick King-Smith,
Ted Hughes and Roald Dahl.

Charlotte Voake

*This is me trying to decide what to do for the letter V. In the end
I did my best to fit in as many things that would go together
reasonably naturally in one scene!*

Charlotte Voake had no formal Art School training,
but her ambition was always to be an illustrator.
Her first book, *The New Red Bike*, was published while
she was still at London University studying for a degree in
Art History. Charlotte's books have
been shortlisted for many prizes.
Her picture book, *Ginger*, won
the under-five category of the
1997 Smarties Book Prize.

Bee Willey

*It was a Wednesday. Whilst I waited for ideas to
unwrap, a warm westerly wind wafted past; the
wicked witch waved from the watering can at the
wolf wallowing on his wedge of watermelon.
(The walrus wiggled his whiskers at me.)
'Want to walk into our world?' she whispered.
I went.*

Bee Willey studied Visual Communication at Bath
Academy of Arts. She has worked as a freelance
illustrator, designed record covers, and illustrated
several outstanding picture books, including *ABC* by
Michael Rosen and *Nonsense Songs* by Edward Lear.

Henrietta X

Words starting with X are extremely rare,
The dictionary page is virtually bare.
If you rack your brains I expect you'll find
That only a handful come to mind
Such as Xmas and Xerox and Xylophones,
And X-rays showing the cracks in bones.
So I thought and I thought, and after a pause
I decided on eXtinct dinosaurs.

Henrietta Webb (Miss X!) read French and History of Art
at Bristol University. She has illustrated a number of
books and magazine articles. She currently works
as a heraldic artist at the College of Arms and is a
designer of enamel boxes.

Selina Young

*My first reaction to illustrating the letter Y was Yuk –
what can I draw that begins with Y? I looked out
of my studio window hoping for inspiration . . . and
there it was, a yacht sailing by. I love drawing yachts.
That was the first Y. Then there was Yellow, that's
my favourite colour. From then on my Y letter was
going to be great fun to illustrate. I had one hiccup.
I think I'm probably a better artist than a writer –
spelling is not my strong point: Gina pointed out that
Y-a-t-c-h is not quite how you spell Yacht . . . the problem
was solved in-house with white paint!*

Selina Young took a post-graduate degree at St Martin's
School of Art. She now works full-time as an illustrator
and writes many of her own picture books.
She lives on South Island, New Zealand.

Zita Newcome

*I really drew the short straw getting the letter Z to illustrate!
I opened the dictionary for help, only to be greeted by Zymosis,
Zdophyte, Zwingli, Zeugma, Zeno and so on. It seemed best to
stick to simpler words which is how I ended up with this crazy
picture, subtitled 'Zany Zita Zooms along on her Zealous
Zebra from the Zoo!'*

*I have a number of highly-talented friends who are dyslexic
and went through the ghastly business of being labelled 'stupid'
at school, in the bad old days before it was recognised. Even
now conventional schooling still seems to let children down
in this area. So the Institute's work and the help it can bring
to families is invaluable.*

Zita Newcome worked abroad as a painter before settling as a
freelance artist in London. She now concentrates on illustrating
children's books, including the highly popular *Toddlerobics*.

aardvark ant anteater apple armadillo ba

boulder brick button camel cart cat co

dandelion deer diamond dinosaur do

eagle eat eggs elephant elk envelop

gingerbread girl goose grass hairy hog

ink insect iron jaguar jeans jumper ketch

kiwi knives knit lion lizard love magic

meteorite mist money moon music n

newt nuthatch orange ostrich otter owl p

pink plates puffin quail queen quill quilt

saxophone seahorse shell shrimp starfish

tortoise trunk umbrella underworld un

verandah villa vines violin volcano

window witch wolf x-ray xylophone ya